# THE JAGS

## The Derby Match

### TOM WATT

**Rising Stars UK Ltd.**
22 Grafton Street, London W1S 4EX
www.risingstars-uk.com

Text, design and layout © 2009 Rising Stars Uk Ltd.
The right of Tom Watt to be identified as the author of this work has been
asserted by him in accordance with the Copyright, Design and Patents Act,
1988.

Published 2009

Publisher: Gill Budgell
Editor: Jane Wood
Text design and typesetting: Clive Sutherland
Illustrator: Michael Emmerson for Advocate Art
Cover design: Burville-Riley Partnership
Cover photograph: Ron Coello at www.coellophotography.co.uk
With special thanks to; Robert Dye, Harry Garner, Tyrone Smith, Lewis
McKenzie, Kobina Crankson and Alex Whyte

With thanks to Tottenham Hotspur for the use of their logo.

British Library Cataloguing in Publication Data.
A CIP record for this book is available from the British Library.

ISBN: 978-1-84680-478-6

Printed in the UK by CPI Bookmarque, Croydon, CR0 4TD

**Mixed Sources**
Product group from well-managed
forests and other controlled sources
www.fsc.org  Cert no. TT-COC-002227
© 1996 Forest Stewardship Council

# Contents

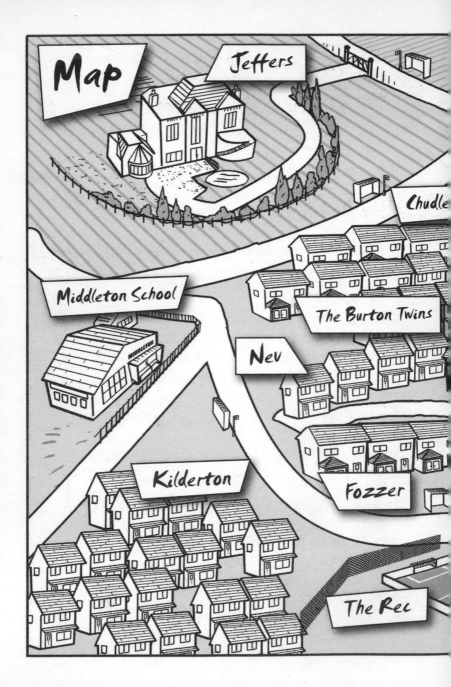

# Meet the Jags

**Andy**

**Name:** Andrew Burton

**Fact:** He's the Jags' captain.

**Loves:** Spurs

**FYI:** The Jags may be his mates, but they'd better not forget he's the Skipper.

**Burts**

**Name:** Terry Burton

**Fact:** He's Andy's twin brother.

**Loves:** Football, football, and more football. He's football crazy!

**FYI:** He's a big Arsenal fan.

**Dev**

**Name:** Ryan Devlin

**Fact:** He's very forgetful.

**Loves:** Daydreaming!

**FYI:** He's always covered in mud and bruises.

### Fozzer

**Name:** Hamed Foster

**Fact:** He can run like crazy, but he shoots like crazy too – sometimes at the wrong goal!

**Loves:** Telling bad jokes.

**FYI:** His best friend is Nev.

### Keeps

**Name:** Jim Ward

**Fact:** He's the Jags' Number One goalie – whether he likes it or not!

**Loves:** Trying to score from his end of the pitch.

**FYI:** He's the tallest member of the Jags.

### Jeffers

**Name:** Jeffrey Gilfoyle Chapman

**Fact:** He's the only one of the Jags who doesn't live on the Chudley Park estate.

**Loves:** Being in the Jags.

**FYI:** He's the Jags' top goal-scorer.

**Nev**

**Name:** Denton Neville

**Fact:** Nev is the Jags' most talented player.

**Loves:** Fozzer's bad jokes.

**FYI:** He keeps his feet on the ground and always looks out for his football crazy mates.

**Mrs Burton**

**Name:** Pam Burton

**Fact:** The Burton twins' mum, and a team 'mum' for all the Jags.

**Loves:** Sorting out her boys.

**FYI:** Doesn't actually like football!

**Mr Ward**

**Name:** Jack Ward

**Fact:** He's Jim's dad and the Jags' coach!

**Loves:** Going on and on, doing his team talks.

**FYI:** He's taking his coaching exams.

# Super Sunday

*Spurs were playing Arsenal and it was live on TV. I'm an Arsenal fan and my brother is a Spurs fan so I couldn't watch the match with him! I went round to Nev's house, he's a Liverpool fan so he didn't mind who won ...*

**Nev**   Well, 1–1 was fair, Burts.
It could have been worse.

**Burts**   Yeah. I bet Andy went crazy when Spurs scored. It's hard having a brother who's a Spurs fan.

**Nev**   It must be just as hard for him.

**Burts**   What? Hard being a Spurs fan?

**Nev**    No, man. Hard having a brother who's an Arsenal fan. I bet you two argue and argue.

**Burts**    Well, it's not too bad. Except when Arsenal and Spurs play each other.

**Nev**    It's lucky for you that Arsenal usually win.

**Burts**    But do you remember when Spurs beat us in the Carling Cup? Andy was singing "5–1, 5–1" for weeks.

**Nev**    Yeah, I remember.
It was terrible.

**Burts**   I had to go to bed with ear-plugs. He was even singing in his sleep!

**Nev**   Why was it such a big deal? It was only the Carling Cup. And it was only Arsenal versus Spurs.

**Burts**   But it's our derby match.

**Nev**   Yeah, but it's not a really big derby match. Not like the Merseyside derby when it's Liverpool versus Everton. That's a really big game.

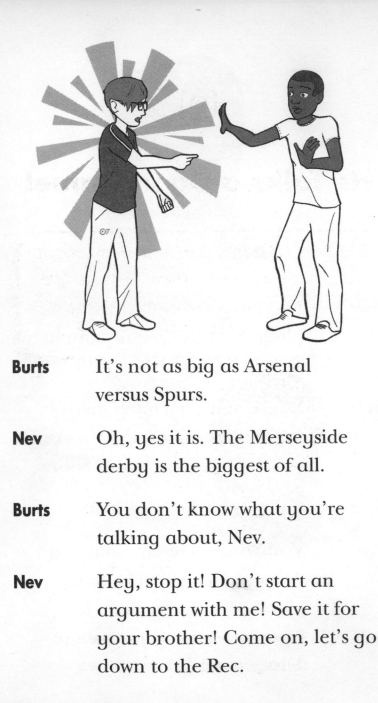

**Burts**    It's not as big as Arsenal versus Spurs.

**Nev**    Oh, yes it is. The Merseyside derby is the biggest of all.

**Burts**    You don't know what you're talking about, Nev.

**Nev**    Hey, stop it! Don't start an argument with me! Save it for your brother! Come on, let's go down to the Rec.

# He Talks a Good Game!

I love football but Burts is crazy about it. He doesn't know when to stop. The good thing is that he'll always come out for a kick-about.

**Burts**     What were you saying about derby matches?

**Nev**    Burts! Forget it. I don't want to argue. I just want to play.

**Burts**  Yeah, I know. Sorry. I can't help it. I'm football crazy.

**Nev**    I noticed, mate. And you've got it bad. Maybe you just need to run about a bit. Take it out on the ball!

**Burts**     Okay. You can go in goal and
              I'll take shots at you.

**Nev**       No way! Let's take it in turns.
              Or we can play one against one.

**Burts**    But you're bigger than me. And you're better than me. I'll never win against you.

**Nev**    What about if I play left-footed?

**Burts**    Okay. I'll be Cesc Fabregas. Who are you going to be?

**Nev**    I'll be Steven Gerrard. You can do all the talking, John Motson.

**Burts** What do you mean?

**Nev** Oh, come on. We all know you love pretending to be a commentator.

**Burts** Yeah, but only to myself.

**Nev**    Well, I've heard you in Jags games. "It's Andy to Fozzer. He crosses. And there's Jeffers to score!"

**Burts**    Well, like I say, I'm football crazy.

**Nev**    Don't worry. I think it's good. It makes it feel like a proper game.

**Burts**    Jags games *are* proper games. But wouldn't it be great if we had a proper derby match, too?

# Haven't You Heard?

We got to The Rec, and played, and played. Nobody else was about, so it was just me and Nev. He's the Jags' best player so I was tired out by the time we stopped.

**Nev**     Let's have five minutes for half-time. Then we can change ends.

**Burts**    I need more than five minutes, Nev. I feel like I've just played Spurs on my own!

**Nev**    You're getting better every time we play, Burts. I bet you didn't even notice that I was using my right foot.

**Burts**    No wonder I'm tired out.

**Nev**    *I* was getting tired out from getting tackled all the time, mate. I had to do something. I couldn't let you win, could I?

**Burts**   What was the score?

**Nev**   I don't know. I thought you were keeping count. Was it 30–something?

**Burts**   No, no. I was in the lead at first. I think it was 23–all.

**Nev**   Yeah. But it's only half-time, remember. I'll get you in the second half.

**Burts**    Not if you play left-footed
again, like you said you would.

**Nev**    I know, I know. Hey, you know
what you were saying about us
having a proper derby match?
Wouldn't it be great?

**Burts**     Maybe we should ask the boys down on Farm Way if they want to get a team up. It could be the Jags versus "The Sheep", or the Jags versus "The Cows".

**Nev**     Or "The Cockerels".

**Burts**     No, not cockerels, because Spurs have a cockerel on their club badge. My brother would want to play for them!

**Nev**   What about that game between our schools? Will that count as a derby?

**Burts**   What game between our schools? Why haven't I heard about it?

# Friend or Foe?

I couldn't believe it! At my school we had been talking for days about Middleton versus Parkside in the Kilderton Schools Cup. But Burts hadn't heard about it.

**Burts**    When was this fixed up?

28

**Nev**     I don't know. Our school heard about it last week. It's at The Vale next Wednesday, I think.

**Burts**   Why didn't anybody tell me?

**Nev**     Maybe you just weren't listening. Or maybe you're not in the Parkside team?

**Burts**   But, but …

**Nev**     I'm joking! Of course you'll be in the team. And if anybody should know about it, it should be you.

**Burts**     I know what's happened. Mr Smart has been off sick. He's in charge of our team. He'll tell us about it when he gets back.

**Nev**     So, do you think your school against my school will count as a derby? I mean, I only play for Middleton now and again. The Jags are our proper team.

**Burts** Of course it will count as a derby. It'll be like England versus Scotland, or Brazil versus Argentina. Middleton versus Parkside is as big as they come.

**Nev**    What? Will they show it on TV?

**Burts**    Maybe they would if Kilderton had its own TV station!

**Nev**    Yeah! And I bet I know who would be doing the commentary. Our very own Terry Burton!

**Burts**    No way. I'd want to play, not talk.

**Nev**    What do you mean? You usually do both! Come on, your five minutes for half-time is up, Burts. I'll be England now. Who are you going to be?

# The Build-up Starts Now!

We carried on playing, Nev and me. The more we played, the better he got. Well, he is the Jags' best player. And I was thinking about the Jags, too. What would happen when we had to play against each other for our schools?

**Nev**        What's the matter, Burts?
Are you tired out already?

**Burts**        Just a bit! One against one is
hard work. Especially when the
other one is Denton Neville.
You were lucky, though.

**Nev**        Lucky? Nev 50, Burts 35? Sounds
pretty easy to me!

**Burts**    No, I mean lucky I didn't show
off my new skills.

**Nev**    Oh, yeah? What new skills?
Tripping me up from behind
when I'm in goal?

**Burts**   No, no, no. The secret skills I've got to save for the big derby match.

**Nev**   What? Middleton against Parkside? How can you have secret skills for that already? You didn't even know about it half an hour ago.

**Burts**   I'm always having good ideas, Nev. I showed Cesc Fabregas everything he knows, remember!

**Nev**   Yeah, right! And Steven Gerrard is always calling me up for tips!

**Burts**   Seriously, Nev. It's going to be hard playing against each other for our schools.

**Nev**   I know. Me and Fozzer and your brother will be on one side. You and Keeps and Dev will be on the other side. It's crazy!

**Burts**   We'll have to remember not to pass to each other. And what if one of us scores an own goal? The school will think it's because we play together for the Jags.

**Nev**    Who's going to score an own goal? Not me!

**Burts**    No, I'm just saying: "What if?". And what if we have arguments?

**Nev**    Like we had arguments about Arsenal versus Spurs, and Liverpool versus Everton?

**Burts**    No, I mean what if we have arguments about Parkside versus Middleton. It'll be a derby, remember.

**Nev**     Yeah, but don't worry, Burts. We only have to play against each other for one game. We're proper team mates for the Jags. And the Jags are for life!

# MIDDLETON 1 PARKSIDE 1

The big match was on Wednesday. It was a great game. Burts couldn't help pretending he was a commentator!

**Burts**  Middleton kick off and head towards the Parkside goal. That's a good shot from Andy Burton, but it just goes wide.

**Nev**  I'm running into the box now, Fozzer. Cross it!

**Burts**    There could be danger here for Parkside.

**Nev**    Yes! I've scored! What a cross! Well done, Fozzer. It's 1–0 to us!

**Burts**    Can Burts and his boys get back in the game and save the match?

*We were in the lead for most of the game. But right at the end, Burts made it 1–1, so we had to share the Cup.*

**Burts**    Well done, Nev. Great game. Great goal.

**Nev**    You too, Burts. I was sure we would beat you. But watch out next year! We'll be back!

# Rivals!

CITY BEAT UNITED

Every football team has a rival that they want to beat most of all! It could be the team from the next school or the next street or the next town. You know each other really well. You are friends off the pitch. But not when it comes to a match!

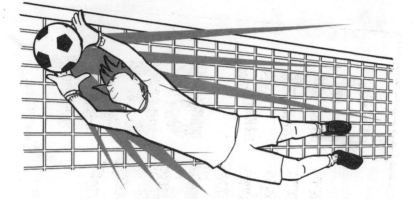

 Football games between big rivals are called "derby" matches. Nobody knows how they got that name. But every player and every fan knows who their own derby match is against.

In the Premier League, a derby match is always full. Everybody wants to see Arsenal versus Spurs or Liverpool versus Everton.

# The Derby Match Quiz

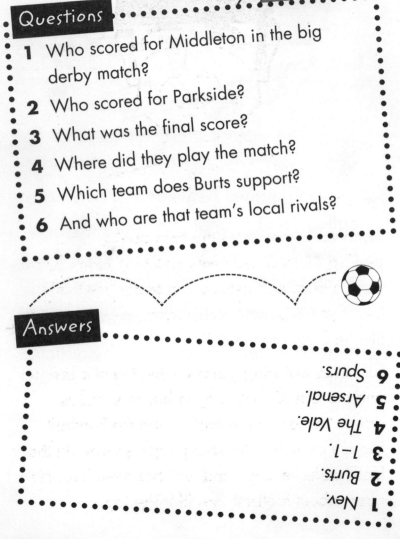

## Questions

1 Who scored for Middleton in the big derby match?

2 Who scored for Parkside?

3 What was the final score?

4 Where did they play the match?

5 Which team does Burts support?

6 And who are that team's local rivals?

## Answers

1 Nev.
2 Burts.
3 1–1.
4 The Vale.
5 Arsenal.
6 Spurs.

# About the Author

Tom Watt, who writes the Jags books, loves playing football. He loves watching football, too. But the team he supports is a secret. He thinks that if you support another team, you might not like his books any more!

Tom likes watching games in the Premier League and the Champions League but he watches games in the Championship and the Football League as well. If he sees people playing in the local park, he stops and watches them, too. He's crazy about football. Just like The Jags.

# THE JAGS

Who's Got My Boots?
A New Striker
The Derby Match
Who's Washing the Kit?
The Big Deal
Star Player Wanted
Your Turn in Goal
The Team Talk
Whose Side Are You On?
Hitting the Headlines
Up for the Cup
The Own Goal